Adding ed

A **verb** is a **doing** or **action** word. When an actio̶
sometimes add **ed** to the verb. For example: Tod̶
yesterday I **helped** Dad.

Write the **verbs** in these sentences to match the p̶i̶c̶
telling someone what happened in the **past**.

jump 	wash 	look 

I .... high. I .... my bike. I .... at my book.

pull 	sort 	plant 

I .... the rope. I .... my old toys. I .... a tree.

play 	rain 	wait 

I .... on a swing. It .... I .... in a queue.

Spot the Speller says

"Some **verbs** change in different ways when
they are talking about the **past**. For example,
sit changes to **sat**, **see** to **saw**, **run** to **ran**
and **am** to **was**. So watch out!"

Adding ing

A **suffix** is a group of letters that can be added to the end of a **root word** to change its meaning. The suffix **ing** can be added to verbs to change them.
For example: A frog can **jump**. It is **jumping**.
Remember: A **root word** is a word to which groups of letters may be added to make other words.
Look at these pictures. Choose the right verb from the box, then write it with the suffix **ing**.

peck pour sleep play climb push read drink sweep

. . . .

. . . .

. . . .

The long **a** sound

One of the spellings for the **long a** sound is **a_e**. The vowels are split by a consonant, as in the word **late**. The letter **e** is written at the end of each word.
Remember: vowels are a, e, i, o, and u. All other letters are consonants.
Complete these words and draw lines joining them to the right picture.

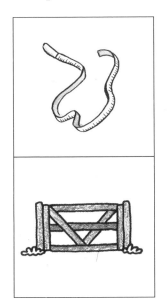

c__k__

sk__t__

g__t__

t__p__

Complete the following sentences.

I h__t__ smelly fish.

I think football is a good g__m__.

Do you know my n__m__?

Joe

Twins can look the s__m__.

Spot the Speller says

"Remember, when you spell any of these words, put the **e** at the end."

3

The long i sound

One of the spellings for the **long i** sound is **i_e**. The vowels are split by a consonant, as in the word line. The letter **e** is written at the end of each word.

Complete these words, and draw lines joining them to the right pictures.

n__n__

w__n__

p__p__

k__t__

f__v__

l__n__

Complete the following sentences.

I had a r__d__ on my b__k__.

I had a big b__t__ of an apple.

Spot the Speller says

"Remember to write the letter **e** at the end with the long **i** sound."

The long e sound

Usually, when the letters **ee** or **ea** are together in a word, they are used for the **long e** sound.

Complete these words, and join them to the right pictures. If you are unsure which spelling to use, write the word both ways to see which looks right.

b__ __

thr__ __

tr__ __

b__ __ns

fl__ __s

r__ __ding

b__ __ch

t__ __ch

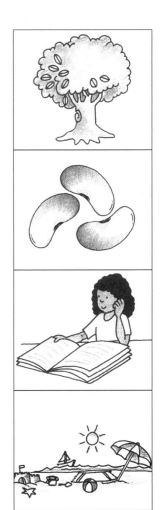

Spot the Speller says

"If the **long e** sound is in a word, then the spelling is probably **ee** or **ea**, but you have to remember which one! Also, remember in some words the **ea** sound is short as in **head**, **bread** and **dead**. What a lot to remember!"

The long o sound

One of the spellings for the **long o** sound is o_e. The vowels are split by a consonant, as in the word **note**. The letter **e** is written at the end of each word.

Complete the words below and join them to the right pictures.

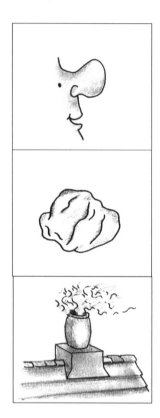

b__n__

c__n__

r__s__

n__s__

sm__k__

st__n__

Complete these sentences using the words from the box below.

| rose   bone   mole   hole |

My dog loves to chew on a ....

A .... is a beautiful flower.

I am a..............., and I like to live in my ....

6

The long **u** sound

One of the spellings for the **long u** sound is **u_e**. The vowels are split by a consonant, as in the word **flute**. The letter **e** is written at the end of each word.

Draw a line to join each word to the right picture.

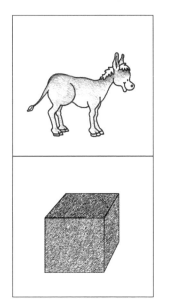

tube

mule

tune

cube

The letters **ew** and **ue** are used for the **long u** sound.

Complete these sentences using the words from the box below.

flew   blue   grew   glue   clue   chew

In the summer, the sky is ....

My little puppy finds it hard to .... a bone.

Jack's beans .... and ....

The little robin .... away when I went too close.

The .... I used was really sticky.

The detective found an important ....

w and the Wonderful Witch

The Wonderful Witch changes how the letter **a** sounds after the letter **w**. She can make the letters **wa** sound like **wo**, as in the word **wat**ch.

Complete these words.

s__ __n

s__ __tter

__ __tch

__ __sp

__ __nd

__ __shing

The Wonderful Witch can also cast a spell to make **wor** sound like **wer**.

Write the missing words into these sentences. Choose from the box below.

| word | worm | world | worship |

I would love to travel around the .... in a rocket.

A .... is very slippery and wiggly, but it has no legs!

Shh! Don't say a .... or you will wake up the baby.

Some people go to a temple or a church to ....

Question words

The following words are used to ask a question:

| why | when | what | which | where | who |

Here are some funny riddles. Fill in the missing question words.

.... did the chicken cross the road?   **To get to the other side.**

Knock ! Knock ! .... is there?   **Aunt.**
Aunt .... ?   **Aren't you ready yet?**

.... is a door not a door?   .... **it is a jar.**

.... would you find the Andes?   **On the ends of your armies.**

.... would you find two apples that are the same? **On a pair tree.**

.... goes up when rain comes down?   **An umbrella.**

.... is yellow and swings through the trees?   **Tarzipan.**

.... is the most dangerous city in the world?   **Electricity.**

Spot the Speller says

"Collect your own
funny riddles, and write
them down so that
you don't forget them!"

Don't get in a muddle

There are many spellings for the sound **air**, as in ch**air**.
For example: **are**, **ere**, **ear** and **air**.

Complete these sentences using the words in the box below.

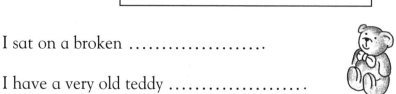

I sat on a broken ....

I have a very old teddy ....

"Go over ....," the teacher said.

Walking in the rain is fun. I don't .... if I get wet.

There are many spellings for the **or** sound. For example: **or**, **oor**, **aw**, **au** and **ore**.

Draw a line joining each word to the right picture.

door

draw

daughter

claw

snore

saw

Find the rule

Look at the **singular** to **plural** changes in the groups of words in the first column below. In the second column, write out the rule for making **plurals** for each group then use it to make each of the words in the last column **plural**.

fishes?

fishyes?

fishies?

fish?

Word endings	The rules	Examples
The **plurals** of words ending in soft sounds, such as **s**, **ss**, **sh**, **ch**, and **x** are made like this: fish → fishes patch → patches box → boxes	....	dish .... match .... fox ....
The **plurals** of words ending in a vowel and **y** are made like this: day → days toy → toys key → keys	....	donkey .... boy .... way ....
The **plurals** of words ending in a consonant and **y** are made like this: lady → ladies baby → babies jelly → jellies	....	granny .... potty .... party ....

11

The prefixes **un** and **dis**

A **prefix** is a group of letters that can be added to the beginning of a **root word** to change its meaning. For example, **un** and **dis** are prefixes meaning "not".

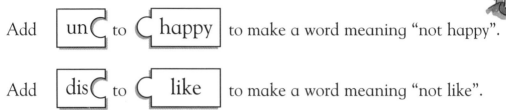

Add **un** to **happy** to make a word meaning "not happy".

Add **dis** to **like** to make a word meaning "not like".

The prefixes **un** and **dis** change a **root word** to its opposite meaning. Use these **prefixes** to make the opposite of each of the words below.

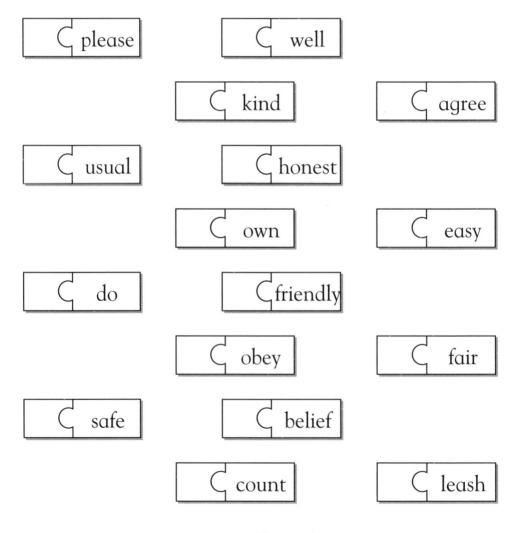

please

well

kind

agree

usual

honest

own

easy

do

friendly

obey

fair

safe

belief

count

leash

12

The prefix **pre**

The prefix **pre** means "before". For example:

$$\boxed{\text{pre} \subset} \ + \ \subset \boxed{\text{fix}} \ = \ \boxed{\text{pre} \subset \text{fix}}$$

A prefix is a group of letters added before a **root word**.

Fill in the missing letters in the following words, which all begin with **pre**.

The time before history was written down

_ _ _ h _ s _ _ _ y

To plan before, to be ready

_ _ _ p _ r _

To make up, to imagine, or to play at being something

_ _ _ t _ n _

To give an award to someone, a gift

_ _ _ s _ n _

To like better, to want more

_ _ _ f _ r

To go, or to be before

_ _ _ c _ _ e

Elected leader of a country, such as the United States

_ _ _ s _ d _ n _

To stop something from happening

_ _ _ v _ n _

To say what will happen before it happens

_ _ _ d _ c _

13

The prefix de

The prefix **de** can mean "down", "below" and "away from". It can also change a **root word** to its opposite meaning. Add the prefix **de** to complete the words on the notebook below.

__ __ stroy   __ __ frost   __ __ sign

__ __ cide   __ __ feat   __ __ scribe

__ __ pend   __ __ ceive   __ __ liver

__ __ crease   __ __ posit

Complete the following sentences using the words above.

I can ....on my good friend.

Mark has to .... a parcel.

Try and............................. what your house looks like.

Ben did not mean to............................. Usha's toys.

We .... new equipment in technology.

The boy told a lie, trying to .... the teacher.

The car driver needed to .... her speed.

I can't ....which clothes to wear.

Gran had to ....the pizza from the freezer.

Ali went to .... the money in the bank.

Team A might .... team B in the match.

14

Contractions

A **contraction** is two words joined together to make one word. One or two letters are taken out. For example:

I am   I'm

Remember: An **apostrophe** is used to replace one or two missing letters.

Join each of the following words in bold to its **contraction**. One has been done for you.

she is

we have

didn't

couldn't

do not

we've

could not

she's

did not

can't

you are

I have

don't

she will

you're

can not

he is

he's

I've

she'll

you will

you'll

Blends and ends

A **blend** is a combination of two or more consonants used together. For example, the letters **g** and **r** are used together to make a **blend** in words such as **gr**owl, **gr**eet and **gr**asp.

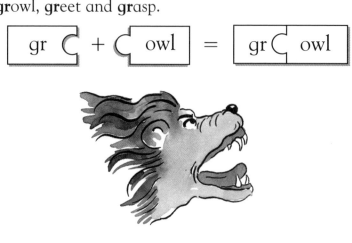

| gr | + | owl | = | gr | owl |

| Blends | Word ends |

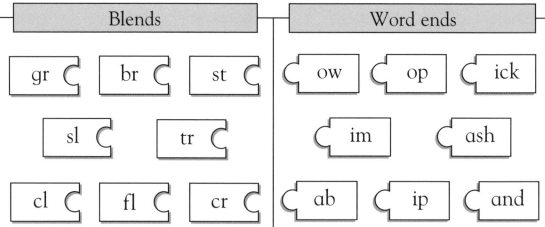

gr	br	st	ow	op	ick
sl	tr	im	ash
cl	fl	cr	ab	ip	and

Join the **blends** to the **word ends** to make new words. Try to make at least 12 words.

....

....

....

....

16

Silent letters

Read the sentences below. Look at the words in bold letters. Cross out the **silent letters** in each of these words. The **silent letters** are the ones we do not pronounce. For example, the **k** in knife is not pronounced.

The **signpost** was bent **halfway** up.

The **honest knight knew** he needed a **sword**.

Lisa cut her **thumb** with a **knife** and went **white** with shock.

I tried to stay **calm** but my **knees** were **knocking**.

We **wrote rhymes** about **gnats**.

Jan should **comb** her hair but I **doubt** she does.

Now write each of these words on the correct line below. Can you think of other words with **silent letters**? Add your own words to the lists.

silent l ....

silent k ....

silent g ....

silent w ....

silent h ....

silent b ....

Spellings to learn							
night	rhymes	slow	doubt	thumb	knew	honest	should

17

Compound words

A **compound word** is formed by joining two short words together to make one longer word. For example:

| day + light | = | day light |

Use the short words below to make 20 **compound words**.

any	light
some	father
day	body
grand	thing
every	shine
out	one
no	side
sun	where
in	time
play	mother

....

....

....

....

....

....

....

....

....

....

Can you make any more **compound words** using other short words?

....

....

....

....

Adjectives with **y** endings

An **adjective** is a word that describes a **noun**. Many **adjectives** can be made by adding **y** to **nouns**.

For example: mess + y = mess y

Remember: A **noun** is a word that names something.

Add **y** to each of the **root words** below to make an **adjective**. Then use the **adjective** to describe something. One has been done for you.

Root word	Adjective	Describe something
sand	sandy	a sandy beach
storm		
lump		
guilt		
smell		
water		
dirt		
fuss		

Adverbs ending in **ly**

An **adverb** is a word that describes a **verb**. It describes how an action is done. For example, in the sentence "Jill walked slowly", the word **slowly** is an **adverb** as it describes how Jill walked.

Remember: A **verb** is a doing or action word.

Add **ly** to these words to make **adverbs**.

brave ....   proper ....

quiet ....   sad ....

actual ....   loud ....

real ....   careful ....

Complete these sentences using the new words you have made above.

We carried the baby ....:

Our teacher said, "Ssh! Talk ...."

I .... enjoyed my tea.

The pop group played ....

We listened .... to the bad news.

The knight fought .... against the giant.

20

The suffixes **er** and **est**

A **suffix** is a group of letters that can be added to the end of a **root word** to change its meaning.

For example:

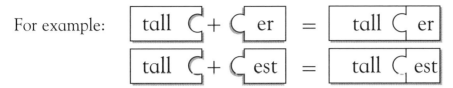

Join each of the root words in bold below to its **er** and **est** forms. One has been done for you.

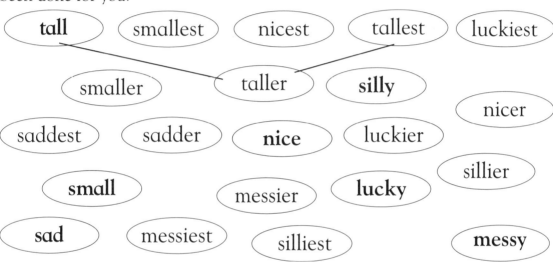

Now sort the words into the following three columns.

Root words	er suffix	est suffix
............tall............	..........taller..........	.........tallest........
....	....	....
....	....	....
....	....	....
....	....	....
....	....	....
....	....	....

The suffixes **ful** and **less**

The suffixes **ful** and **less** can be added to **root words** to make new words.
The suffix **ful** means "full of " and the suffix **less** means "without".
Remember: ful is like the word **full** but with just one **l**.

For example: cheer + ful = cheer ful

    fear + less = fear less

Add either **ful** or **less** to each of these **root words** to make new words.

Roots	New words
spot	....
success	....
breath	....
help	....
fear	....
care	....

Use the new words above in sentences of your own.

....

....

....

....

....

Root words

Find the words that have the same **root word** and write them under the correct group heading below.

Remember: A **root word** is a word to which groups of letters may be added to make other words.

happily   friends   enjoyable   writes

written   writing

likeness   terrible   joyful

friendly   happiness

unhappy   enjoyment   terrorise

likes   unlikely

writer   liked   enjoying

unfriendly   terrify

terrific   befriend   happiest

friend	like	write
. . . .	. . . .	. . . .
. . . .	. . . .	. . . .
. . . .	. . . .	. . . .
. . . .	. . . .	. . . .

happy	joy	terror
. . . .	. . . .	. . . .
. . . .	. . . .	. . . .
. . . .	. . . .	. . . .
. . . .	. . . .	. . . .

Homophones

Homophones are words that sound the same but have different spellings and meanings.

For example: | hole | and | whole | ; | wait | and | weight |

Look at the **homophone** pairs in the balloons.
Complete these sentences using these words.

hour   our   see   sea

We played with .... friends.

We played outside for an ....

We can .... the beach.

I played in the ....

Write four sentences using the **homophones** in the balloons below.

for

four

knew

new

....

....

....

....

....

....

Can you think of some more **homophone** pairs?

....

....

Rhyming words

Read the words in the book below. Find the seven pairs of **rhyming words** and write them on the lines. Time yourself. How long does it take you to match and write all the rhyming pairs?

rough   dear   sound   earn
proud   weary   wear   dreary
learn   loud   tough
bear   round   fear

.... | ....

.... | ....

.... | ....

.... | Pairs found in [ ] seconds.

Now find seven groups of three **rhyming words** on this list. Time yourself.

....

....

....

....

....

....

....

Groups found in [ ] seconds.

sight   applause
should   nice
thigh   your
ice
high   pause
four
pour
bright   would
mice   weight
cause
light
sigh   eight
could   freight

Verb endings

A verb is a **doing** or **action** word. It tells us what happens in a sentence. It can have different endings.

The endings tell us if the **action** happened in the **past** | she played | ,

or if the **action** happens in the **present** | she plays | ,

or if the **action** is still happening | she is playing | .

Make three new words from each **root verb** by adding the different endings. One has been done for you.

Root verbs	Add **s**	Add **ed**	Add **ing**
shout	.....shouts.....	....shouted....	...shouting....
look	....	....	....
climb	....	....	....
kick	....	....	....
learn	....	....	....
cook	....	....	....
wait	....	....	....
laugh	....	....	....
clean	....	....	....

Rules about verb endings

When adding **ed** or **ing** to **root verbs**, there are some rules to remember.

For most **root verbs**, just add **ed** or **ing**.
For example: cook → cook**ed** → cook**ing**

For **root verbs** ending with a short vowel and a consonant, such as **op**, **ab**, **at** or **it**, double the last letter and then add **ed** or **ing**.
For example: stop → stop**ped** → stop**ping**

Now use these rules to add **ed** and **ing** to each of the root **verbs** below.

Root verbs	Add **ed**	Add **ing**
drop	....	....
call	....	....
fit	....	....
grab	....	....
jump	....	....
hop	....	....
trap	....	....
slip	....	....
play	....	....

More rules about verb endings

Verbs can be changed by adding **s** or **es**, but there are some rules to remember.

For most **verbs**, just add **s**. For example:	I add → She add**s**
For a **verb** ending in a consonant and **y**, change the **y** to **i,** then add **es**. For example:	I worry → She worr**ies**
For a **verb** ending in a soft sound, such as **ss, sh, ch** and **x**, add **es**. For example:	I fix → He fix**es**

Use the rules above to change the following **root verbs**.

I look → She ....   I wish → Carla ....

I help → He ....   I catch → It ....

I pass → Liam ....   I cry → He ....

I find → She ....   I make → It ....

I envy → He ....   I try → She ....

I want → Jo ....   I change → It ....

I rush → He ....   I carry → Carol ....

I play → She ....   I push → He ....

I run → He ....   I fall → She ....

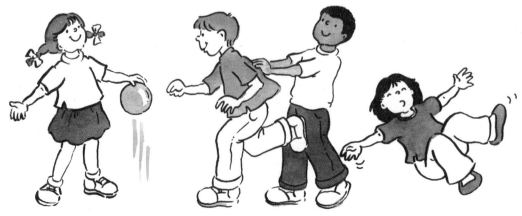

28

Making verbs

Some **nouns** and **adjectives** can be made into **verbs** by adding **suffixes**.
A **suffix** is a group of letters that can be added to the end of a **root word** to change its meaning.

For example: **apology** (noun) + **ise** = apologise
　　　　　　　deep (adjective) + **en** = deepen

Remember: A **noun** is a word that names something.
　　　　　　　An **adjective** is a word that describes a noun.

Draw a line to match each of the **verbs** in the box to a **noun** or an **adjective**.

Nouns	Verbs	Adjectives
	accommodate	
criticism		special
	decorate	
accommodation		real
	realise	
reality		hard
	specialise	
decoration		pure
	loosen	
identity		loose
	criticise	
education		sad
	sadden	
	identify	
	educate	
	purify	
	harden	

The **ight** and **tion** endings

Two common word endings are **ight** and **tion**. How many words can you make
by joining the endings **ight** or **tion** to each of the beginnings below? List the words
in the numbered spaces. Can you fill all the spaces?

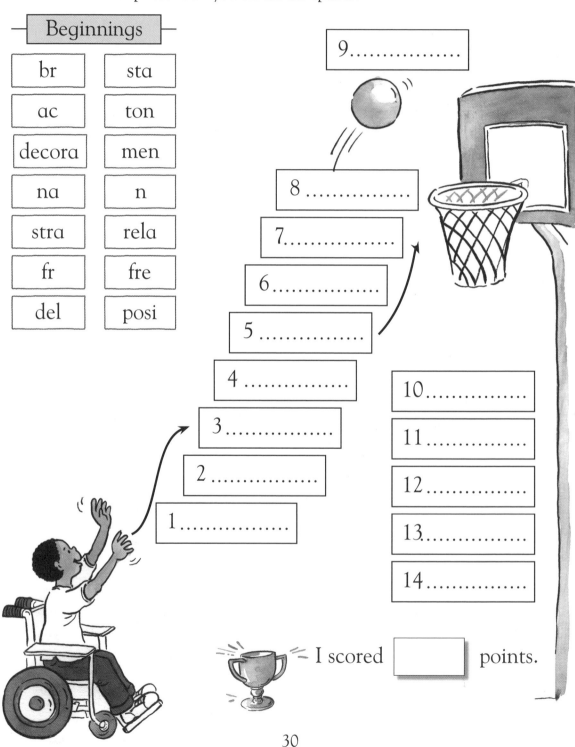

Beginnings

br	sta
ac	ton
decora	men
na	n
stra	rela
fr	fre
del	posi

9................

8 ....

7................

6................

5 ....

4 ....

3................

2 ....

1................

10................

11 ....

12................

13................

14................

I scored ⬚ points.

Suffix rules

This chart shows how some **root words** change when **suffixes** are added.

Root word endings	Adding suffixes to root words	
	If the suffix starts with a vowel	If the suffix starts with a consonant
Some root words end in **e**. For example: **care**	Remove the final e. For example: **caring**	Just add the suffix. For example: **careful**
Some root words end in a vowel and **y**. For example: **play**	Just add the suffix. For example: **player**	Just add the suffix. For example: **playful**
Some root words end in a consonant and **y**. For example: **pretty, beauty, marry**	Change **y** to **i**, except when adding **ing**. For example: **prettiest, marrying**	Change **y** to **i**, then add the suffix. For example: **beautiful**
Some root words end in a short vowel and a consonant. For example: **fit, stop**	Double the final consonant. For example: stopping	Just add the suffix. For example: **fitness**

Add each of these **root words** to its **suffix** using the rules in the chart above.

become + ing = ...   busy + est = ...

hope + ful = ...   annoy + ing = ...

bad + ly = ...   extreme + ist = ...

wet + er = ...   forget + ful = ...

31

Similar suffixes

Some suffixes sound similar, such as **ible** and **able**; tion and **sion**.

Complete the following words using **ible** or **able**. Use a dictionary to check your answers.

terr............   comfort............

reason............   imposs............

sens............   remark............

suit............   laugh............

vis............   horr............

poss............   agree............

Did you notice that **able** usually follows a root word that makes sense on its own? For example, **agree** makes sense on its own. The suffix **ible** usually follows a root that is not an actual word. For example, if you take the **ible** from **horrible**, it leaves **horr**.

Complete the following words using **tion** or **sion**. Use a dictionary to check your answers.

divi............   televi............

explo............   competi............

informa............   protec............

inven............   inva............

revi............   na............

ten............   ac............

vi............   publica............

Making plurals

For singular nouns that end in **f**, **ff** or **fe**, there are three rules to remember when making them plural.

If the word ends in a single **f**, you usually change **f** to **v** and add **es**.	If the word ends in **fe**, change **fe** to **ves**.	If the word ends in **ff**, just add **s**.

For example:

scarf

scarves

For example:

wife

wives

For example:

cuff

cuffs

Write the plurals for these singular nouns.

one leaf → many ....

one thief → many ....

one cliff → many ....

one loaf → many ....

one sniff → many ....

one shelf → many ....

one knife → many ....

33

It's and its

Write its or it's in these sentences.

Tomorrow .... my birthday.

The cup stands on .... saucer.

.... raining again.

The football team changed .... football kit.

Write three sentences of your own using **it's**.

....

....

....

Write three sentences of your own using **its**.

....

....

....

Compound words

A **compound word** is formed by joining two short words together to make one new word. For example:

(foot | ball) is made from (foot) and (ball)

Make **compound words** from the words below, and write them in the bubbles provided. Start by filling the bubble at the bottom of the page. For each **compound word** you make, the ball is kicked closer to the goal. Can you make enough **compound words** to kick the ball into the goal?

Words

after	bed
foot	back
cloak	to
ball	noon
step	side
wards	room

10................

9................

8................

7................

6................

5................

4................

3................

2................

1................

The **shon** and **shan** suffixes

Words ending in **cian, sion** and **tion** all make a **shon** or **shan** sound.

tion is the most common ending. For example: **celebrate** → **celebration**
sion is used when the root word ends in **d, de, s** or **se**. For example: **supervise** → **supervision**
cian is used when a root word ends in c. For example: **magic** → **magician**

Which of the three suffixes finishes off each of the following words? Complete the words.

direc ⟶ ....

divi ⟶ ....

inven ⟶ ....

posi ⟶ ....

televi ⟶ ....

sta ⟶ ....

atten ⟶ ....

politi ⟶ ....

ac ⟶ ....

electri ⟶ ....

pen ⟶ ....

rela ⟶ ....

discus ⟶ ....

opti ⟶ ....

ten ⟶ ....

musi ⟶ ....

Plural search

When changing **singular** nouns into **plurals**, there are some more rules to remember.

Some nouns ending in **o** have **plurals** that end in es.	tomato → tomatoes
Some words ending in **f** form **plurals** by changing the **f** to **v** and adding **es**.	thief → thieves
Some **plurals** do not follow any rule. They are called **irregular plurals**.	child → children

Look at the word puzzle below. Find the plural of each of the ten nouns in the box below, and draw a ring around it.

potato   mouse   hero   knife   shelf
man   tooth   wolf   woman   goose

s	b	m	c	p	v	i	p	k	e
r	o	i	e	u	l	f	i	y	s
n	m	c	a	h	o	l	n	s	h
g	e	e	s	e	d	u	n	k	e
c	n	r	r	r	o	l	k	o	l
e	e	d	w	o	m	e	n	w	v
w	o	l	v	e	s	a	i	i	e
a	r	m	a	s	q	i	v	e	s
d	i	s	n	d	t	e	e	t	h
p	o	t	a	t	o	e	s	o	t

Mnemonic making

One way of remembering the spellings of tricky words is to make up a sentence using the letters. For example, you can learn how to spell **because** by remembering:

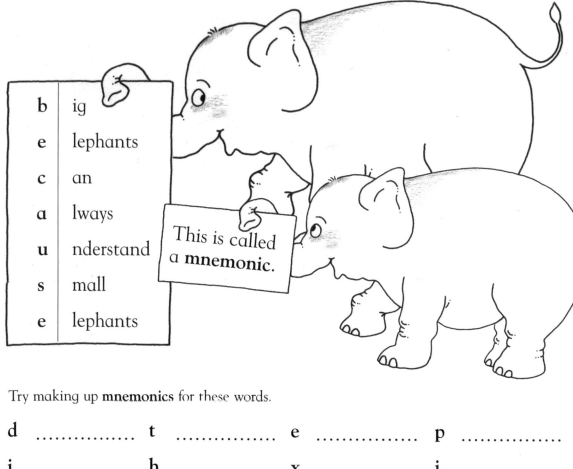

b	ig
e	lephants
c	an
a	lways
u	nderstand
s	mall
e	lephants

This is called a **mnemonic**.

Try making up **mnemonics** for these words.

d	....	t	....	e	....	p	....
i	....	h	....	x	....	i	....
f	....	r	....	c	....	e	....
f	....	o	....	i	....	c	....
e	....	u	....	t	....	e	....
r	....	g	....	e	....	s	....
		h	....	d	....		

What other **mnemonics** can you make? Use a separate sheet of paper.

Spelling Made Easy
Notes for Parents

This 10-page section provides answers or explanatory notes to all the activities in this book. This will enable you to assess your child's work.

Point out any spelling mistakes as you mark each page. As well as making corrections, it it very important to praise your child's efforts and achievements.

Encourage your child to use a dictionary if they get stuck. Suggest that he or she uses a notebook to compile a word bank of new words or difficult spellings.

Play the games from the **Spelling Made Easy** kit with your child to improve their spelling even further.

Adding ed

A **verb** is a **doing** or **action** word. When an action happened in the past, we sometimes add **ed** to the verb. For example: Today I will **help** Mum, because yesterday I **helped** Dad.

Write the **verbs** in these sentences to match the pictures. Pretend you are telling someone what happened in the **past**.

jump — I .....jumped..... high.
wash — I ...washed... my bike.
look — I ..looked.. at my book.
pull — I ...pulled... the rope.
sort — I .sorted. my old toys.
plant — I ....planted.... a tree.
play — I ..played.. on a swing.
rain — It ...rained... .
wait — I ...waited. in a queue.

Spot the Speller says

"Some **verbs** change in different ways when they are talking about the **past**. For example, **sit** changes to **sat**, **see** to **saw**, **run** to **ran** and **am** to **was**. So watch out!"

1

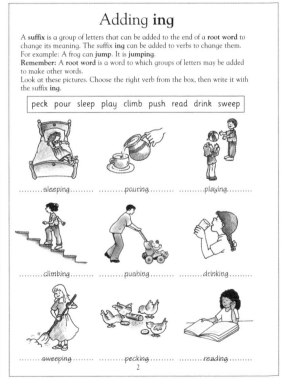

Adding ing

A **suffix** is a group of letters that can be added to the end of a **root word** to change its meaning. The suffix **ing** can be added to verbs to change them. For example: A frog can **jump**. It is **jumping**.
Remember: A **root word** is a word to which groups of letters may be added to make other words.
Look at these pictures. Choose the right verb from the box, then write it with the suffix **ing**.

peck pour sleep play climb push read drink sweep

.........sleeping......... ....pouring......... ....playing.........

.........climbing......... ....pushing......... ....drinking.........

.........sweeping......... ....pecking......... ....reading.........

2

Check that your child knows the meaning of the word verb – an action word. Discuss with your child when to use the past tense of a verb. For independent writing, your child needs to remember the exceptions to the add ed rule.

This page introduces the word suffix – a group of letters added to the ends of words. For example, the suffix ing is added to verbs. While your child is writing the words, encourage him or her to say them aloud as this will reinforce learning them.

ANSWERS

The long a sound

One of the spellings for the **long a** sound is a_e. The vowels are split by a consonant, as in the word **late**. The letter **e** is written at the end of each word.
Remember: vowels are a, e, i, o, and u. All other letters are consonants.
Complete these words and draw lines joining them to the right picture.

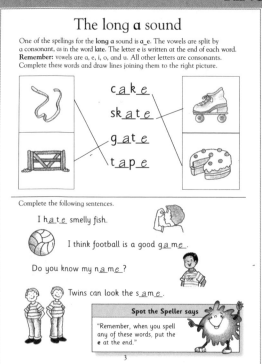

c a k e
sk a t e
g a t e
t a p e

Complete the following sentences.

I h a t e smelly fish.

I think football is a good g a m e.

Do you know my n a m e?

Twins can look the s a m e.

Spot the Speller says
"Remember, when you spell any of these words, put the **e** at the end."

3

The activities on this page focus on the spelling a_e for the long a sound. Ask your child to complete the words with the long a sound and to match them to the right pictures. Encourage him or her to say the words aloud.

The long i sound

One of the spellings for the **long i** sound is i_e. The vowels are split by a consonant, as in the word **line**. The letter **e** is written at the end of each word.

Complete these words, and draw lines joining them to the right pictures.

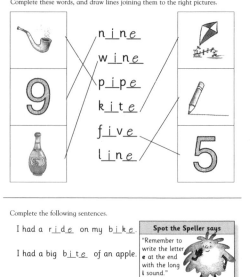

n i n e
w i n e
p i p e
k i t e
f i v e
l i n e

Complete the following sentences.

I had a r i d e on my b i k e.

I had a big b i t e of an apple.

Spot the Speller says
"Remember to write the letter **e** at the end with the long **i** sound."

4

The activities on this page focus on the spelling i_e for the long i sound. Your child completes the words by adding i_e, and then matches the words to the pictures. Your child may like to continue this activity by making other new words.

The long e sound

Usually, when the letters **ee** or **ea** are together in a word, they are used for the **long e** sound.

Complete these words, and join them to the right pictures. If you are unsure which spelling to use, write the word both ways to see which looks right.

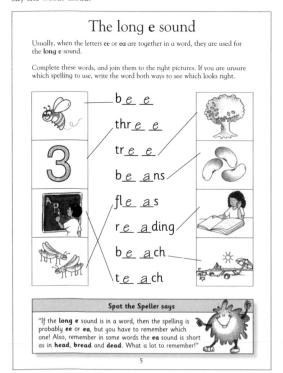

b e e
thr e e
tr e e
b e a ns
fl e a s
r e a ding
b e a ch
te a ch

Spot the Speller says
"If the **long e** sound is in a word, then the spelling is probably **ee** or **ea**, but you have to remember which one! Also, remember in some words the **ea** sound is short as in **head**, **bread** and **dead**. What a lot to remember!"

5

The activity on this page introduces the spelling patterns ee and ea for the long e sound. This page reinforces the need for your child to look as well as listen when remembering spellings. Spot points out that the spelling ea can also be a short e sound.

The long o sound

One of the spellings for the **long o** sound is o_e. The vowels are split by a consonant, as in the word **note**. The letter **e** is written at the end of each word.

Complete the words below and join them to the right pictures

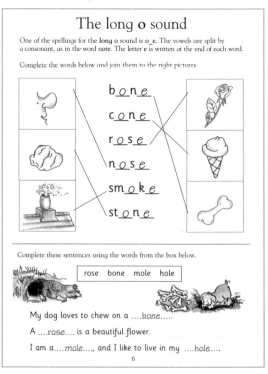

b o n e
c o n e
r o s e
n o s e
sm o k e
st o n e

Complete these sentences using the words from the box below.

rose   bone   mole   hole

My dog loves to chew on a ....bone.....

A ....rose.... is a beautiful flower.

I am a....mole...., and I like to live in my ....hole....

6

The activities on this page focus on the spelling o_e for the long o sound. Your child completes the words by adding o_e and joins the words to the pictures. He or she then completes the sentences in the second activity.

40

ANSWERS

The long **u** sound

One of the spellings for the **long u** sound is u_e. The vowels are split by a consonant, as in the word **flute**. The letter **e** is written at the end of each word.

Draw a line to join each word to the right picture.

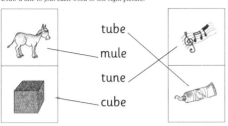

tube
mule
tune
cube

The letters **ew** and **ue** are used for the **long u** sound.

Complete these sentences using the words from the box below.

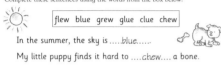

flew blue grew glue clue chew

In the summer, the sky is .....blue......

My little puppy finds it hard to ....chew.... a bone.

Jack's beans ....grew.... and ....grew.....

The little robin .....flew..... away when I went too close.

The ....glue..... I used was really sticky.

The detective found an important .....clue.....

7

This page looks at the spelling patterns for the long u sound: u_e, ew and eu. Encourage your child to both look at and say the words. You can reinforce these spellings by making illustrated lists of additional words.

w and the Wonderful Witch

The Wonderful Witch changes how the letter **a** sounds after the letter **w**. She can make the letters **wa** sound like **wo**, as in the word wa**tch**.

Complete these words.

s_w_a n   s_w_a tter   _w_ tch

_w_ asp   _w_ a nd   _w_ a shing

The Wonderful Witch can also cast a spell to make **wor** sound like **wer**.

Write the missing words into these sentences. Choose from the box below.

word   worm   world   worship

I would love to travel around the ....world.... in a rocket.

A .....worm.... is very slippery and wiggly, but it has no legs!

Shh! Don't say a .....word...or you will wake up the baby.

Some people go to a temple or a church to ...worship...

8

When w is put before a vowel, the vowel sound in a word can change – wa becomes a wo sound, and wor becomes a wer sound. Encourage your child to say the words aloud while completing this activity.

Question words

The following words are used to ask a question:

why   when   what   which   where   who

Here are some funny riddles. Fill in the missing question words.

..Why.......... did the chicken cross the road?   **To get to the other side.**

Knock ! Knock ! ..Who.......... is there?   **Aunt.**
Aunt .who........... ?   **Aren't you ready yet?**

..When........ is a door not a door?   ..When........ it is a jar.

..Where....... would you find the Andes?   **On the ends of your armies.**

..Where....... would you find two apples that are the same? **On a pair tree.**

..What........ goes up when rain comes down?   **An umbrella.**

..What........ is yellow and swings through the trees?   **Tarzipan.**

..Which........ is the most dangerous city in the world?   **Electricity.**

Spot the Speller says

"Collect your own funny riddles, and write them down so that you don't forget them!"

9

This page introduces question words. Jokes and riddles will help your child to select and spell the correct word. Spot encourages your child to collect and write out other rhymes, riddles and jokes.

Don't get in a muddle

There are many spellings for the sound **air**, as in ch**air**. For example: are, ere, ear and air.

Complete these sentences using the words in the box below.

chair   there   care   bear

I sat on a broken ......chair.......

I have a very old teddy ....bear........

"Go over ......there......," the teacher said.

Walking in the rain is fun. I don't ....care....... if I get wet.

There are many spellings for the **or** sound. For example: or, oor, aw, au and ore.

Draw a line joining each word to the right picture.

door
draw
daughter
claw
snore
saw

10

This page looks at different spellings for the air sound and the or sound. It is important that as your child learns to spell more words, she or he can easily recall these differing letter combinations.

Find the rule

Look at the **singular** to **plural** changes in the groups of words in the first column below. In the second column, write out the rule for making **plurals** for each group then use it to make each of the words in the last column **plural**.

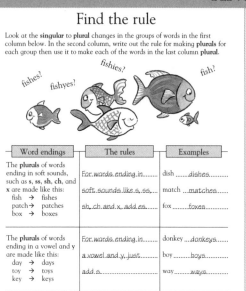

fishes? fishyes? fishies? fish!

Word endings	The rules	Examples
The **plurals** of words ending in soft sounds, such as **s**, **ss**, **sh**, **ch**, and **x** are made like this: fish → fishes patch → patches box → boxes	For words ending in soft sounds like s, ss, sh, ch and x, add es	dish ...dishes... match ...matches... fox ...foxes...
The **plurals** of words ending in a vowel and **y** are made like this: day → days toy → toys key → keys	For words ending in a vowel and y, just add s	donkey ...donkeys... boy ...boys... way ...ways...
The **plurals** of words ending in a consonant and **y** are made like this: lady → ladies baby → babies jelly → jellies	For words ending in a consonant and y, change y to i and add es	granny ...grannies... potty ...potties... party ...parties...

11

Understanding how spelling rules operate on certain words helps children to remember them. Your child should look at how the words are changed, and then write the rules in his or her own words.

The prefixes **un** and **dis**

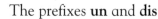

A **prefix** is a group of letters that can be added to the beginning of a **root word** to change its meaning. For example, **un** and **dis** are prefixes meaning "not".

Add [un] to [happy] to make a word meaning "not happy".

Add [dis] to [like] to make a word meaning "not like".

The prefixes **un** and **dis** change a **root word** to its opposite meaning. Use these **prefixes** to make the opposite of each of the words below.

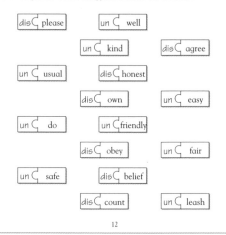

dis please | un well
un kind | dis agree
un usual | dis honest
dis own | un easy
un do | un friendly
dis obey | un fair
un safe | dis belief
dis count | un leash

12

To decide which prefix to use, your child could try saying the word with each prefix and then think about which one sounds right. Encourage your child to check his or her answers in a dictionary.

The prefix **pre**

The prefix **pre** means "before". For example:

[pre] + [fix] = [prefix]

A prefix is a group of letters added before a **root word**.

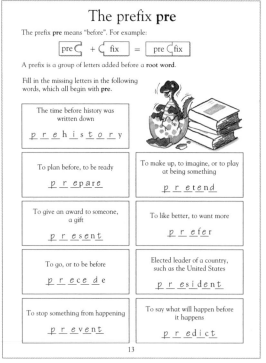

Fill in the missing letters in the following words, which all begin with **pre**.

The time before history was written down p r e h i s t o r y	
To plan before, to be ready p r e p a r e	To make up, to imagine, or to play at being something p r e t e n d
To give an award to someone, a gift p r e s e n t	To like better, to want more p r e f e r
To go, or to be before p r e c e d e	Elected leader of a country, such as the United States p r e s i d e n t
To stop something from happening p r e v e n t	To say what will happen before it happens p r e d i c t

13

Your child needs to read each definition, and consider which word beginning with pre it describes. Before starting, your child may find it helpful to think of words that begin with pre.

The prefix **de**

The prefix **de** can mean "down", "below" and "away from". It can also change a **root word** to its opposite meaning. Add the prefix **de** to complete the words on the notebook below.

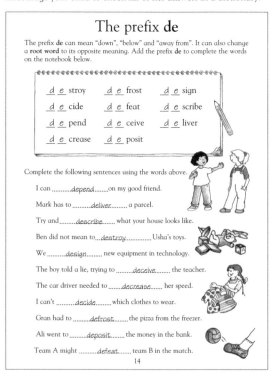

d e stroy	d e frost	d e sign
d e cide	d e feat	d e scribe
d e pend	d e ceive	d e liver
d e crease	d e posit	

Complete the following sentences using the words above.

I can ...depend... on my good friend.

Mark has to ...deliver... a parcel.

Try and ...describe... what your house looks like.

Ben did not mean to ...destroy... Usha's toys.

We ...design... new equipment in technology.

The boy told a lie, trying to ...deceive... the teacher.

The car driver needed to ...decrease... her speed.

I can't ...decide... which clothes to wear.

Gran had to ...defrost... the pizza from the freezer.

Ali went to ...deposit... the money in the bank.

Team A might ...defeat... team B in the match.

14

By adding the de prefix to these roots, your child will make words he or she recognises. Encourage him or her to read the roots before adding the prefix, and then learn the words.

Contractions

A **contraction** is two words joined together to make one word. One or two letters are taken out. For example:

I am   I'm

Remember: An **apostrophe** is used to replace one or two missing letters.

Join each of the following words in bold to its **contraction**. One has been done for you.

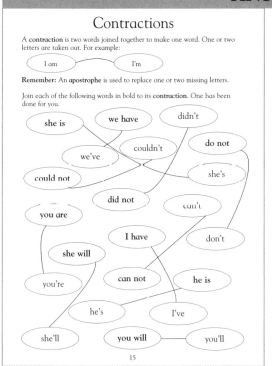

she is   we have   didn't

couldn't   do not

we've

could not   she's

did not   can't

you are

I have   don't

she will

you're   can not   he is

he's   I've

she'll   you will   you'll

15

Your child needs to remember how the apostrophe is used and where it is positioned in contractions. Point out that the apostrophe in I'm replaces the a in the am of I am.

Blends and ends

A **blend** is a combination of two or more consonants used together. For example, the letters **g** and **r** are used together to make a **blend** in words such as **gr**owl, **gr**eet and **gr**asp.

gr + owl = growl

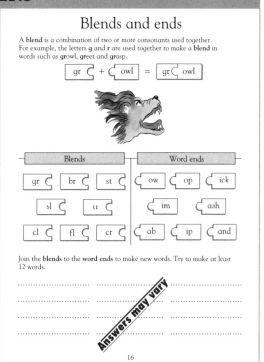

Blends			Word ends		
gr	br	st	ow	op	ick
sl		tr		im	ash
cl	fl	cr	ab	ip	and

Join the **blends** to the **word ends** to make new words. Try to make at least 12 words.

Answers may vary

16

Blends of two or more consonant sounds are often used in words. Although individual sounds can be identified, they run together smoothly in a blend, such as bl in the words black and blue.

Silent letters

Read the sentences below. Look at the words in bold letters. Cross out the **silent letters** in each of these words. The **silent letters** are the ones we do not pronounce. For example, the **k** in knife is not pronounced.

The si**g**npost was bent hal**f**way up.

The **h**onest **k**night **k**new he needed a s**w**ord.

Lisa cut her thum**b** with a **k**nife and went **w**hite with shock.

I tried to stay ca**l**m but my **k**nees were **k**nocking.

We **w**rote r**h**ymes about **g**nats.

Jan should com**b** her hair but I dou**b**t she does.

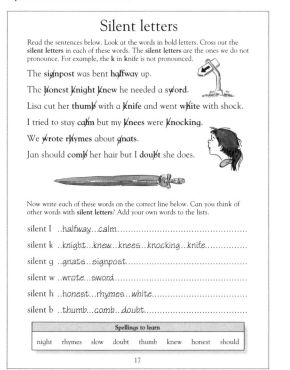

Now write each of these words on the correct line below. Can you think of other words with **silent letters**? Add your own words to the lists.

silent l ..halfway...calm............................

silent k ..knight...knew...knees...knocking...knife...............

silent g ..gnats...signpost............................

silent w ..wrote...sword............................

silent h ..honest...rhymes...white............................

silent b ..thumb...comb...doubt............................

Spellings to learn							
night	rhymes	slow	doubt	thumb	knew	honest	should

17

Help your child identify the letter that can't be heard by encouraging him or her to look closely at each bold word while saying it aloud. Your child could break the word into its letter sounds.

Compound words

A **compound word** is formed by joining two short words together to make one longer word. For example:

day + light = daylight

Use the short words below to make 20 **compound words**.

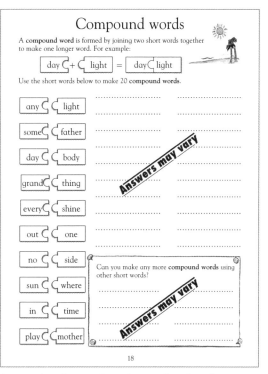

any   light

some   father

day   body

grand   thing

every   shine

out   one

no   side

sun   where

in   time

play   mother

Answers may vary

Can you make any more **compound words** using other short words?

Answers may vary

18

Compound words are made up of two small words, such as anything. Your child should realise that if he or she can spell the two small words, then he or she can spell the compound word.

Adjectives with y endings

An **adjective** is a word that describes a **noun**. Many **adjectives** can be made by adding y to **nouns**.

For example: [mess C] + [C y] = [mess C y]

Remember: A **noun** is a word that names something.

Add **y** to each of the **root words** below to make an **adjective**. Then use the **adjective** to describe something. One has been done for you.

Root word	Adjective	Describe something
sand	sandy	a sandy beach
storm		
lump		
guilt		
smell		
water		
dirt		
fuss		

Answers may vary

19

As with ing, adding y to the end of roots is uncomplicated and generates many new words. Explain the idea of an adjective and help your child to use it before a noun.

Adverbs ending in ly

An **adverb** is a word that describes a **verb**. It describes how an action is done. For example, in the sentence "Jill walked slowly", the word **slowly** is an **adverb** as it describes how Jill walked.
Remember: A **verb** is a doing or action word.

Add **ly** to these words to make **adverbs**.

brave ......bravely...................... proper ......properly......................

quiet ......quietly...................... sad ....sadly......................

actual ...actually...................... loud ....loudly......................

real ......really...................... careful ......carefully......................

Complete these sentences using the new words you have made above.

We carried the baby ......carefully......:

Our teacher said, "Ssh! Talk ......quietly......."

I ....really........enjoyed my tea.

The pop group played ....loudly........:

We listened ....sadly........to the bad news.

The knight fought ......bravely......against the giant.

20

To complete the sentences, your child will need to think about each adverb and then of the action it could describe. To do this, he or she could ask "When would I use the adverb properly?"

The suffixes **er** and **est**

A **suffix** is a group of letters that can be added to the end of a **root word** to change its meaning.

For example: [tall C] + [C er] = [tall C er]
[tall C] + [C est] = [tall C est]

Join each of the root words in bold below to its **er** and **est** forms. One has been done for you.

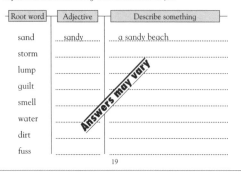

Now sort the words into the following three columns.

Root words	er suffix	est suffix
tall	taller	tallest
sad	sadder	saddest
small	smaller	smallest
nice	nicer	nicest
lucky	luckier	luckiest
messy	messier	messiest
silly	sillier	silliest

21

The er form, called the comparative, is used when comparing two things. The est form, called the superlative, is used when comparing three or more things, "Tom is taller than Jill, but I am the tallest".

The suffixes **ful** and **less**

The suffixes **ful** and **less** can be added to **root words** to make new words. The suffix **ful** means "full of " and the suffix **less** means "without".
Remember: ful is like the word **full** but with just one **l**.

For example: [cheer C] + [C ful] = [cheer C ful]
[fear C] + [C less] = [fear C less]

Add either **ful** or **less** to each of these **root words** to make new words.

Roots	New words
spot	spotless
success	successful
breath	breathless
help	helpful or helpless
fear	fearful or fearless
care	careful or careless

Use the new words above in sentences of your own.

....

....

....

....

....

Answers may vary

22

Your child practises making words with the suffixes ful and less. Some roots are only used with one of the suffixes, others will take either. Remind your child about using the one l in ful.

Root words

Find the words that have the same **root word** and write them under the correct group heading below.
Remember: A **root word** is a word to which groups of letters may be added to make other words.

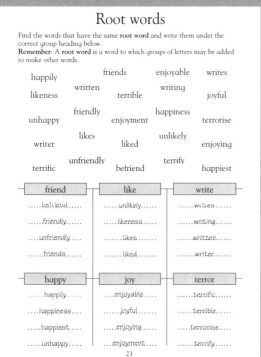

happily	friends	enjoyable	writes
likeness	written	writing	joyful
unhappy	terrible		
friendly	happiness		
enjoyment			terrorise
writer	likes	unlikely	
	liked		enjoying
terrific	unfriendly	terrify	
	befriend		happiest

friend	like	write
....befriend.....	....unlikely......	......written......
.....friendly......	....likeness.....	......writing......
....unfriendly....	......likes.......	.....written......
......friends......	......liked.......	.....writer.....

happy	joy	terror
......happily......	...enjoyable.....	......terrific......
....happiness....	....joyful........	......terrible......
.....happiest.....	....enjoying......	....terrorise.....
....unhappy.....	...enjoyment....	.....terrify......

23

Words with similar meanings contain similar spelling patterns. As your child does this activity, you could discuss the meanings and identify the similarities with him or her.

Homophones

Homophones are words that sound the same but have different spellings and meanings.

For example: hole and whole ; wait and weight

Look at the **homophone** pairs in the balloons. Complete these sentences using these words.

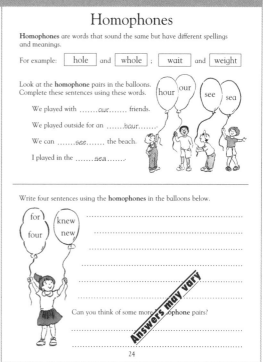

hour our see sea

We played with ....our....... friends.

We played outside for an ....hour........

We can ....see....... the beach.

I played in the ....sea.......

Write four sentences using the **homophones** in the balloons below.

for knew
four new

Answers may vary

Can you think of some more ....ophone pairs?

24

Homophones can cause confusion. Before your child writes the sentences, read and say the words with him or her. You can make notes on the page, distinguishing one spelling from another.

Rhyming words

Read the words in the book below. Find the seven pairs of **rhyming words** and write them on the lines. Time yourself. How long does it take you to match and write all the rhyming pairs?

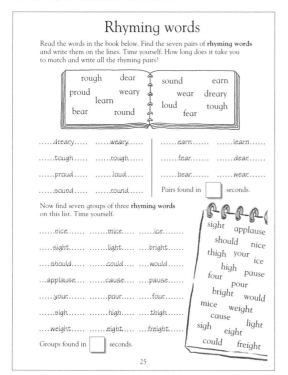

rough	dear	sound	earn
proud	weary	wear	dreary
learn	loud	tough
bear	round	fear

.....dreary..... ......weary......   ......earn...... ......learn......
......tough..... ......rough......   ....fear....... ......dear......
......proud..... ......loud......   ......bear...... ......wear......
......sound..... ......round.....   Pairs found in ☐ seconds.

Now find seven groups of three **rhyming words** on this list. Time yourself.

......nice...... ......mice...... ......ice.......
....sight...... ....light..... ....bright....
....should..... ....could.... ....would....
...applause... ......cause.... ....pause......
......your...... ......pour..... .....four.....
......sigh...... ......high.... ....thigh......
....weight..... ....eight.... ...freight....

Groups found in ☐ seconds.

sight applause
should nice
thigh your ice
high pause
four pour
bright would
mice weight
cause light
sigh eight
could freight

25

Similar looking strings of letters can make completely different sounds. Check your child is matching words by their sound and not by how they look. You could read the words together.

Verb endings

A verb is a **doing** or **action** word. It tells us what happens in a sentence. It can have different endings.

The endings tell us if the **action** happened in the **past** she played ,

or if the **action** happens in the **present** she plays ,

or if the **action** is still happening she is playing .

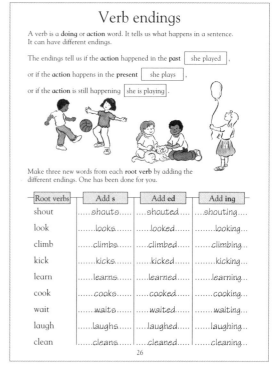

Make three new words from each **root verb** by adding the different endings. One has been done for you.

Root verbs	Add s	Add ed	Add ing
shout	....shouts.....	....shouted....	...shouting....
look	....looks......	....looked......	......looking...
climb	....climbs.....	....climbed.....	......climbing...
kick	.....kicks......	.....kicked......	......kicking...
learn	....learns.....	....learned.....	....learning...
cook	....cooks.....	....cooked.....	....cooking...
wait	....waits.....	....waited.....	....waiting...
laugh	....laughs.....	.....laughed.....	....laughing...
clean	....cleans.....	.....cleaned.....	.....cleaning...

26

The three endings s, ed and ing are the basis for spelling different forms of verbs. Extend the activity by asking your child to make sentences using the three different forms.

45

Rules about verb endings

When adding **ed** or **ing** to **root verbs**, there are some rules to remember.

> For most **root verbs**, just add **ed** or **ing**.
> For example: cook → cooked → cooking

> For **root verbs** ending with a short vowel and a consonant, such as **op**,
> **ab**, **at** or **it**, double the last letter and then add **ed** or **ing**.
> For example: stop → stopped → stopping

Now use these rules to add **ed** and **ing** to each of the root **verbs** below.

Root verbs	Add ed	Add ing
drop	dropped	dropping
call	called	calling
fit	fitted	fitting
grab	grabbed	grabbing
jump	jumped	jumping
hop	hopped	hopping
trap	trapped	trapping
slip	slipped	slipping
play	played	playing

27

Words ending in a short vowel and a consonant make confusing exceptions to spelling rules. Saying the vowels in their short sound form, such as o in shop and i as in pit, makes a, e, i, o, u sound different.

More rules about verb endings

Verbs can be changed by adding **s** or **es**, but there are some rules to remember.

For most **verbs**, just add **s**. For example:	I add → She adds
For a **verb** ending in a consonant and **y**, change the **y** to **i**, then add **es**. For example:	I worry → She worries
For a **verb** ending in a soft sound, such as **ss**, **sh**, **ch** and **x**, add **es**. For example:	I fix → He fixes

Use the rules above to change the following **root verbs**.

I look →	She looks	I wish →	Carla wishes
I help →	He helps	I catch →	It catches
I pass →	Liam passes	I cry →	He cries
I find →	She finds	I make →	It makes
I envy →	He envies	I try →	She tries
I want →	Jo wants	I change →	It changes
I rush →	He rushes	I carry →	Carol carries
I play →	She plays	I push →	He pushes
I run →	He runs	I fall →	She falls

28

The addition of s sometimes has to be modified to avoid unpronounceable words like pushs and catchs.

Making verbs

Some **nouns** and **adjectives** can be made into **verbs** by adding **suffixes**.
A **suffix** is a group of letters that can be added to the end of a **root word** to change its meaning.
For example: apology (noun) + ise = apologise
                      deep (adjective) + en = deepen
Remember: A **noun** is a word that names something.
                    An **adjective** is a word that describes a noun.

Draw a line to match each of the **verbs** in the box to a **noun** or an **adjective**.

Nouns	Verbs	Adjectives
	accommodate	
criticism		special
	decorate	
accommodation		real
	realise	
reality		hard
	specialise	
decoration		pure
	loosen	
identity		loose
	criticise	
education		sad
	sadden	
	identify	
	educate	
	purify	
	harden	

29

This activity shows the connections between grammar and spelling. By adding a suffix, a word can change from one part of speech to another, as shown in the noun to verb to adjective connections.

The **ight** and **tion** endings

Two common word endings are **ight** and **tion**. How many words can you make by joining the endings **ight** or **tion** to each of the beginnings below? List the words in the numbered spaces. Can you fill all the spaces?

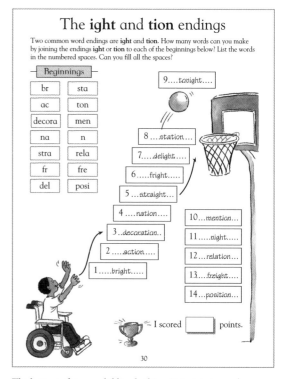

Beginnings	
br	sta
ac	ton
decora	men
na	n
stra	rela
fr	fre
del	posi

9. tonight

8. station

7. delight

6. fright

5. straight

4. nation

3. decoration

2. action

1. bright

10. mention

11. night

12. relation

13. freight

14. position

I scored [ ] points.

30

The best way for your child to do this activity is to try each beginning with both endings. He or she can then discard unreal words, such as menight, but use the real words, such as mention.

ANSWERS

Suffix rules

This chart shows how some **root words** change when **suffixes** are added.

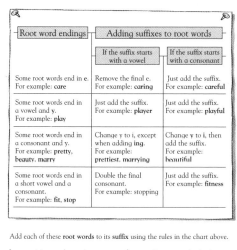

Root word endings	Adding suffixes to root words	
	If the suffix starts with a vowel	If the suffix starts with a consonant
Some root words end in e. For example: **care**	Remove the final e. For example: **caring**	Just add the suffix. For example: **careful**
Some root words end in a vowel and y. For example: **play**	Just add the suffix. For example: **player**	Just add the suffix. For example: **playful**
Some root words end in a consonant and y. For example: **pretty, beauty, marry**	Change y to i, except when adding **ing**. For example: **prettiest, marrying**	Change y to i, then add the suffix. For example: **beautiful**
Some root words end in a short vowel and a consonant. For example: **fit, stop**	Double the final consonant. For example: stopping	Just add the suffix. For example: **fitness**

Add each of these **root words** to its **suffix** using the rules in the chart above.

become + ing = ..*becoming*....   busy + est = ..*busiest*.......

hope + ful = ..*hopeful*.......   annoy + ing = ..*annoying*.....

bad + ly = ..*badly*.........   extreme + ist = ..*extremist*....

wet + er = ..*wetter*........   forget + ful = ..*forgetful*.....

31

These rules should be learnt. As your child works through each example at the end of the page, encourage him or her to identify which part of the chart explains the rule for each word.

Similar suffixes

Some suffixes sound similar, such as **ible** and **able**; **tion** and **sion**.

Complete the following words using **ible** or **able**. Use a dictionary to check your answers.

terr*ible*......   comfort*able*......

reason*able*......   imposs*ible*......

sens*ible*......   remark*able*......

suit*able*......   laugh*able*......

vis*ible*......   horr*ible*......

poss*ible*......   agree*able*......

Did you notice that **able** usually follows a root word that makes sense on its own? For example, **agree** makes sense on its own. The suffix **ible** usually follows a root that is not an actual word. For example, if you take the **ible** from **horrible**, it leaves **horr**.

Complete the following words using **tion** or **sion**. Use a dictionary to check your answers.

divi*sion*......   televi*sion*......

explo*sion*......   competi*tion*......

informa*tion*......   protec*tion*......

inven*tion*......   inva*sion*......

revi*sion*......   na*tion*......

ten*sion*......   ac*tion*......

vi*sion*......   publica*tion*......

32

The "actual word" rule is a way of differentiating between words with the ible or able endings. Encourage your child to say each root word aloud and consider whether it is an "actual word".

Making plurals

For singular nouns that end in **f**, **ff** or **fe**, there are three rules to remember when making them plural.

If the word ends in a single **f**, you usually change **f** to **v** and add **es**.	If the word ends in **fe**, change **fe** to **ves**.	If the word ends in **ff**, just add s.
For example:	For example:	For example:
scarf	wife	cuff
scarves	wives	cuffs

Write the plurals for these singular nouns.

one leaf → many ..*leaves*.......

one thief → many ..*thieves*......

one cliff → many ..*cliffs*.........

one loaf → many ..*loaves*.......

one sniff → many ..*sniffs*.........

one shelf → many ..*shelves*......

one knife → many ..*knives*.......

33

The v plurals are often misspelt, but remembering the rules helps your child to distinguish them. Having tried these, he or she could try making plurals of other words, ending with ff or fe.

It's and its

It's	Its
It's (with an **apostrophe**) is a shortened form of **it is**. The **apostrophe** marks the place where one or more letters have been taken out. In **it's**, the **apostrophe** marks the place of the missing **i**.	**Its** (without an apostrophe) is a **possessive** word. A **possessive** word tells us who or what something belongs to. For example, in "The dog eats **its** food", the word **its** tells us that the food belongs to the dog.

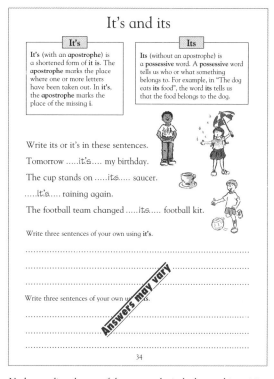

Write its or it's in these sentences.

Tomorrow .....*it's*.... my birthday.

The cup stands on .....*its*..... saucer.

.....*It's*.... raining again.

The football team changed .....*its*..... football kit.

Write three sentences of your own using **it's**.

....

....

....

Write three sentences of your own u~~sing its.~~

Answers may vary

....

....

....

34

Understanding the use of the apostrophe is the key to this activity. Encourage your child to read the information, which will help him or her to distinguish between it's and its.

47

Compound words

A **compound word** is formed by joining two short words together to make one new word. For example:

| foot | ball | is made from | foot | and | ball |

Make **compound words** from the words below, and write them in the bubbles provided. Start by filling the bubble at the bottom of the page. For each **compound word** you make, the ball is kicked closer to the goal. Can you make enough **compound words** to kick the ball into the goal?

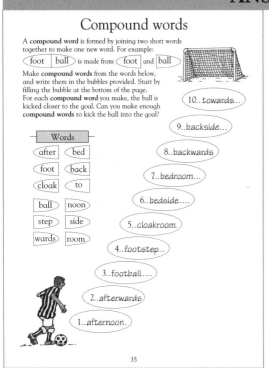

Words

after	bed
foot	back
cloak	to
ball	noon
step	side
wards	room

10...towards..

9..backside...

8..backwards

7..bedroom...

6..bedside....

5..cloakroom.

4..footstep...

3..football....

2..afterwards

1..afternoon.

35

To extend this activity, encourage your child to look for other compound words in the dictionary. Can he or she find other words that begin or end with the words given in this activity?

The **shon** and **shan** suffixes

Words ending in **cian**, **sion** and **tion** all make a **shon** or **shan** sound.

| **tion** is the most common ending. For example: **celebrate → celebration** |
| **sion** is used when the root word ends in **d, de, s** or **se**. For example: **supervise → supervision** |
| **cian** is used when a root word ends in **c**. For example: **magic → magician** |

Which of the three suffixes finishes off each of the following words? Complete the words.

direc → .direction........
divi → .division...........
inven → .invention........
posi → .position...........
televi → .television........
sta → .station...........
atten → .attention.........
politi → .politician........
ac → .action............
electri → .electrician.......
pen → .pension..........
rela → .relation..........
discus → .discussion......
opti → .optician..........
ten → .tension...........
musi → .musician.........

36

Encourage your child to refer to the rules. The key to this activity is for him or her to think how the root words end. For example, direc is from the root direct, ending in t, so the suffix must be tion.

Plural search

When changing **singular** nouns into **plurals**, there are some more rules to remember.

Some nouns ending in o have **plurals** that end in es.	tomato → tomatoes
Some words ending in f form **plurals** by changing the f to v and adding **es**.	thief → thieves
Some **plurals** do not follow any rule. They are called **irregular plurals**.	child → children

Look at the word puzzle below. Find the plural of each of the ten nouns in the box below, and draw a ring around it.

| potato | mouse | hero | knife | shelf |
| man | tooth | wolf | woman | goose |

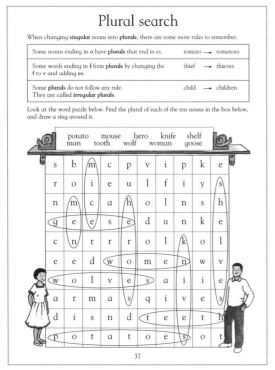

s	b	m	c	p	v	i	p	k	e
r	o	i	e	u	l	f	i	y	s
n	m	c	a	h	o	l	n	s	h
g	e	e	s	e	d	u	n	k	e
c	n	r	r	r	o	l	k	o	l
e	e	d	w	o	m	e	n	w	v
w	o	l	v	e	s	a	i	i	e
a	r	m	a	s	q	i	v	e	s
d	i	s	n	d	t	e	e	t	h
p	o	t	a	t	o	e	s	o	t

37

Reading the list of singular nouns and saying their plurals will help your child find the difference between those words with an s ending and those that change completely, such as tooth to teeth.

Mnemonic making

One way of remembering the spellings of tricky words is to make up a sentence using the letters. For example, you can learn how to spell **because** by remembering:

b	ig
e	lephants
c	an
a	lways
u	nderstand
s	mall
e	lephants

This is called a **mnemonic**.

Try making up **mnemonics** for these words.

d	....	t	....	e	....	p	....
i	....	h	....	x	....	i	....
f	....	r	....			e	....
f	....	o	....			c	....
e	....	u	....	t	....	e	....
r	....	g	....	e	....	s	....
		h	....	d			

Answers may vary

What other **mnemonics** can you make? Use a separate sheet of paper.

38

To extend this activity, encourage your child to write mnemonics for words that he or she finds difficult. Put the separate sheet of paper up on a wall to be referred to regularly.